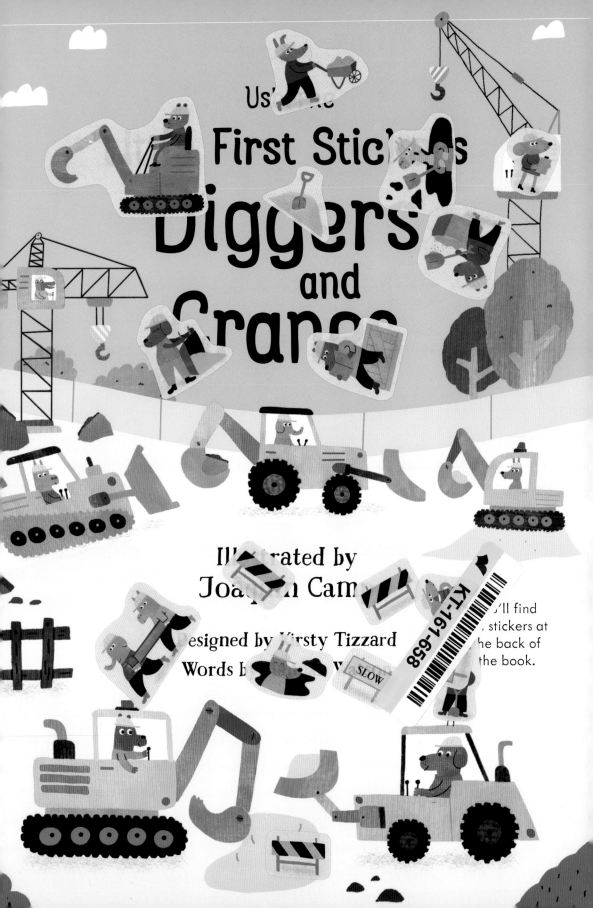

Usborne
First Stickers
Diggers
and
Cranes

Illustrated by
Joaquín Cam...

...esigned by Kirsty Tizzard

Words b...

...'ll find
...stickers at
...he back of
the book.

Lifting and loading

In this scrapyard, cranes sort old cars so their parts can be used again. Stick on some cranes lifting cars and collecting metal.

...ne to pick up this old car.

Add a magnet crane collecting metal.

Carrying cargo

At the port, big cranes are used to load cargo on to ships. Add lots of busy workers moving crates of fruit.

4

Stick some cranes on the ship's deck.

Fill this road with trucks.

Snowdrift

Diggers m[...]he rescue to clear the snow b[...]oad. Find a tow truck to p[...] of a snowdrift, too.

Stick on a crane collecting logs.

Add a digger tipping snow into this truck.

Find a big crane to help move the tree.

Building higher

Cranes are needed to complete these new buildings. They will be the tallest in the town. Finish the picture with stickers.

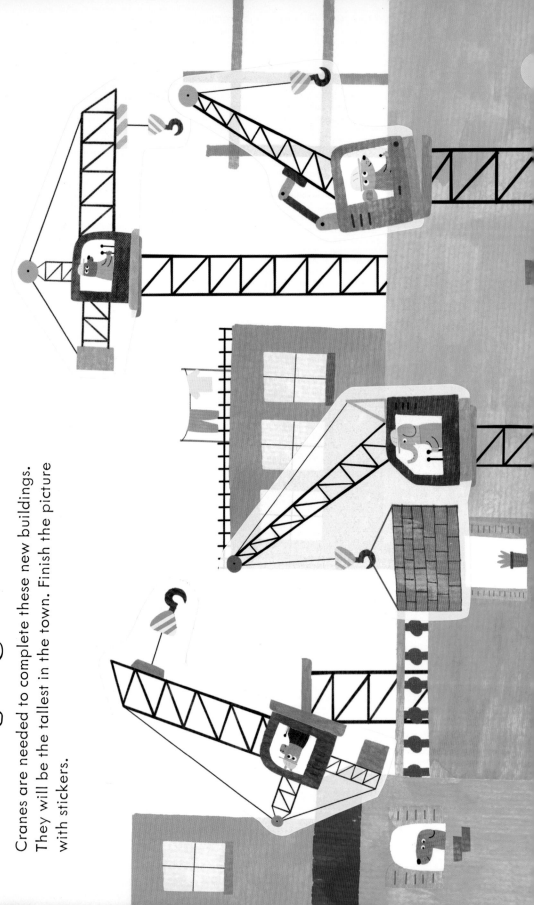

Stick a crane lifting bricks on this rooftop.

Find a window for this crane to lift.

9

Roadworks

The water pipes under the road need to be fixed. Add diggers to clear away the soil, and a crane to lift new pipes into place.

BOOKS

Find a cra...

...jam along this...

11

In a quarry

Diggers scoop out heavy pieces of rock from
the quarry. They will be used to make buildin
Add lots of diggers trundling up this track.

SLOW

SLOW

13

Demolition

Cranes, diggers and other big machines are needed to pull down old buildings so new ones can be built.

CAUTION

Max capacity
2 animals

Stick on some
overseeing

Find lots of cranes to demolish this building.

...tor to pull... ...to safety.

Playground

Add lots of machines to this picture
to help build a playground.

Find a crane lifting a roundabout.

Add a digger
filling a sandpit.

Lifting and loading pages 2-3

Carrying cargo pages 4-5

Snowdrift pages 6-7

Building higher pages 8-9

Roadworks pages 10-11

In a quarry pages 12-13

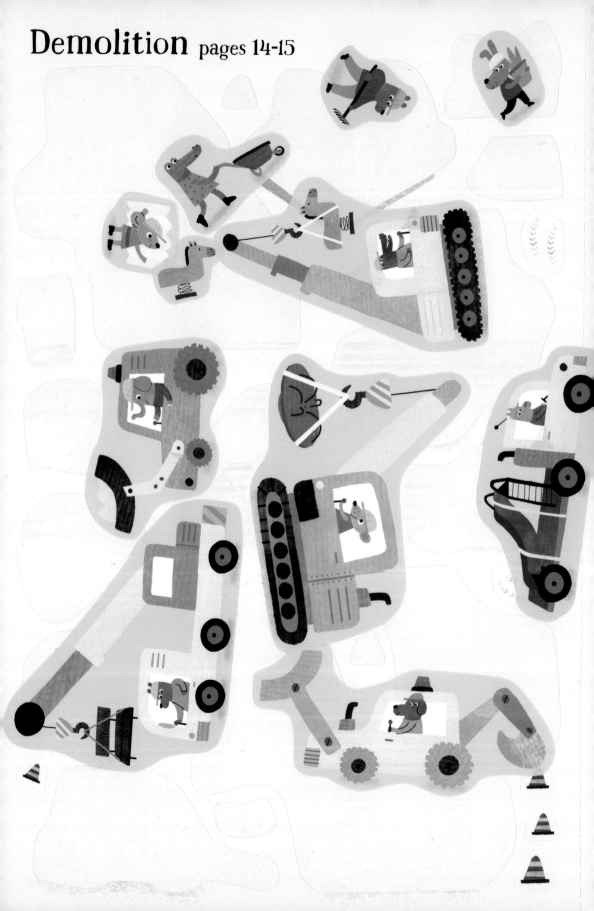

Demolition pages 14-15

Playground page 16

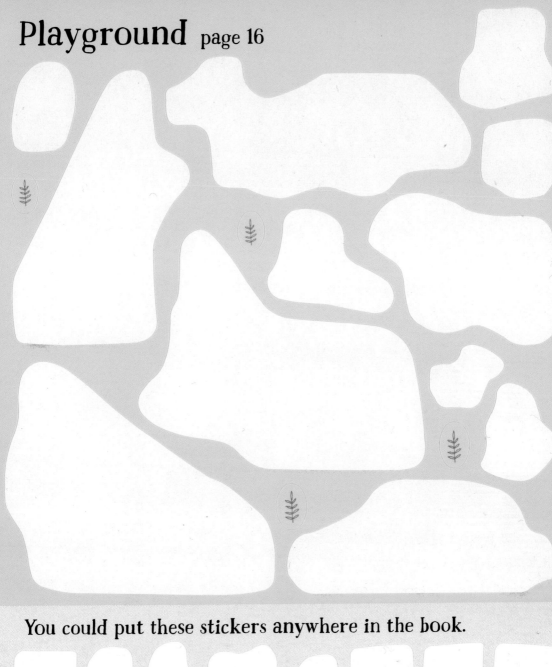

You could put these stickers anywhere in the book.